WE THE WILD ONES

is a book of STORIES and POEMS and ART describing

the TRUE ADVENTURES of a child, a cat, and the

WANDERING WIND in the overgrown

gardens of childhood including the EPIC TALES

'HIGH IN THE OLD OAK TREE'

and

'DAISY AND THE WAYWARD WIND'

and

· *the remarkable* true story of

JAMBORANJA JAMBORAM:

"Sometimes he's a crow, sometimes he's a man"

and

some various short myths and moments

remembered by The Wild Ones and recorded in verse.

Written *and* drawn *by*

ED BOXALL

Published by The Pearbox Press, 2023

50 Edmund Road, Hastings, TN35 5LF

EDBOXALL.CO.UK

**Pearbox
Books**

WE THE WILD ONES

Ed Boxall

For Sophia, go wild! from Ed Boxall

CONTENTS

WE THE WILD ONES

We the Wild Ones are on the run

From walls and roofs and electric light

We don't need school or shops or cars

Because we are not civilised

We don't wear shoes our feet are tough

We walk wherever wonder leads

Away forever far and free

We the Wild Ones, Cat and Me!

Morning Bits

When I am asleep I fall apart.
My legs

                                             arms

        head

 spine

                                fingers

      liver

       heart

                                      eyes

    mouth

         and all my other bits are scatterred
like space debri floating aimlessly
across the dark universe.

As I wake up
my bits travel light years to find each other again
and slot together as they tumble up
into daylight.

They somehow always
find the same human shape
as last time
I was awake.

Amazing.

Wendell Wodee

In the morning
Wendell Wodee
the wise old pigeon
coos

take this day
to enjoy your world
first take off your
shoes

stretch your toes
across the ground
the grass is fresh and
cool

let go of plans
see what the day
might want to play with
you

THE STORY OF
JAMBORANJA JAMBORAM

Jamboranja Jamboram
The Creature Coloured By Sky Dreams
The Great Jamboranja

Jamboranja Jamboram

I follow the paths of badgers and cats,
Down through the brambles by the railway tracks.
There's an old beech tree hung with painted cans,
Where there lives Jamboramba Jamboram.

A strange wind rises when people come close,
To warn him to turn back into a crow.
But when he sees it's me he caws hello,
And leaps from the branches to the ground below.

Hey Jamboranja Jamboram,
Sometimes you're a crow,
Sometimes you're a man.

He has a spangle trumpet of yellow and gold,
And a Beard of Remembers made of bright rope.
He's got a rat and a wren living in his coat,
A stick and a drum and a book of bad jokes.

We like to break into Cooper's Scrapyard,
And play cassette tapes in the abandoned cars.
We dance with the scarecrows and the shooting stars,
To Ziggy Stardust and the Spiders from Mars.

17

Hey Jamboranja
Hey Jamboranja
Hey Jamboranja
JAMBORAM

Hey Jamboranja   Hey Jamboranja

What are you today?   A crow or a man?

We collect the rubber bands the posties drop,
As we walk towards nowhere until we get lost.
We are making up a world called *Yondermoss*,
And its sagas of the sleeves and the woolly socks.

Best of all the derelict days,
A feeling in the air the weather will break.
We wait in the tree for the drops of rain,
A storm will release our power to change.

Then we will be the only birds,
To brave the storm's rush and swirl.
We will dive and dance and swoop and curl,
Far above the limits of the human world!

Hey Jamboranja Jamboram!
We three crows were once
A boy, a cat and a man

The Creature Coloured by Sky Dreams

By Jamboranja Jamboram

After long days pretending to be,
Like all the other children in class,
I would come home to Father who was busy at his work,
In his study but as distant as the stars.

So I would scramble under brambles and damp beech leaves,
To find the Creature Coloured by Sky Dreams,
Her feathers would flutter with sunset colours,
Pink gold and crimson in the breeze.

She showed the special way to spread my arms,
So my restless unbelonging became wings,
We would blend with the sky as she taught me how to fly,
And to dance my own dance with the wind.

Together we flew over the horizon,
To the endless other lands of Unsomewhere,
Where I rested in the light of her high bright realm,
Of soft singing sighs and smistral air.

Until my unbelonging drove me on,
To set free the restless clown from inside me,
So I became The Great Jamboranja,
And left for the fairs and city streets.

I joked, jumped, and juggled for tatter natter crowds,
In my fire and sparkle travelling show,
The people gasped and screamed on wizz and flicker nights,
When I turned into a sunset coloured crow.

But one day I thought I heard the far impatient voice,
Of Father calling me to chop wood,
So I flew home but found a hundred years gone,
And a railway where our house once stood.

Now I cannot find the way back to Unsomewhere,
Without The Creature Coloured by Sky Dreams,
So I live in this beech tree by the railway track,
Where my feathers flutter black in the breeze.

THE GREAT JAMBORANJA

Remembered by Jamboranja Jamboram

LADEEEEEES AND GENTLEMAN FOR JUST A FEW PENNIES
AND THE SIGHT OF YOUR WIDE, DELIGHTED EYES
I WILL AMAZE
I WILL ASTOUND
I WILL PROVIDE
THE BEST SHOW OF YOUR LIVES!
I WILL BREATHE FIRE THROUGH MY NOSE
AND SMOKE THOUGH MY EYES
MY FIREWORK FINGERS WILL LIGHT UP THE SKIES.
But I will admit...
...this is all a trick
(I was taught by the
Dragons of Briddecky Crick).

But when the moon rises and the night is still
I will spread my arms and they will turn to wings

And this my friends is **not** a trick.
You will see me become a rainbow crow
I will carry your hearts where they need to go
to find new life, new dreams, new hope.

FOR I AM THE ONLY, THE SYMPHOSTRATAL
THE GREAT JAMBORANJA !

! See ! The ! Great ! Jamboranja ! ; ! ; !

In the Town Square

At Sunset

Bungalow Brown

Bungalow Brown was a sparrow,
Who lived in Old Thundersley,
A medium sized village,
On the outskirts of Southend-on-Sea.

He was friends with Mr Ormorod,
Who liked old stamps and steam trains,
And growing pumpkins in his garden,
Where he wore a smart tie every day.

Memory Common

Moments meander through time,
Like balloons blown over the fields,
That sometimes get caught in the branches,
Of the Memory Common oak trees.

Like when I saw Mr Ormorod and a sparrow,
Share a piece of cheese,
And the train to India rattled away,
Billowing clouds of white steam.

High in the Old Oak Tree

One day I heard the old oak tree,

Singing with the breeze,

A whispering sigh of swaying leaves sang,

Will you climb me please?

Will you climb me please?

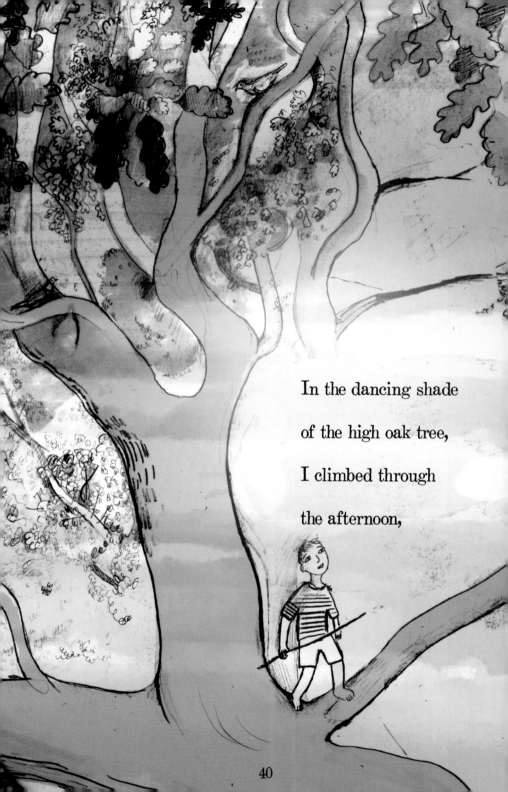

In the dancing shade

of the high oak tree,

I climbed through

the afternoon,

I made my bed in its strong arms,

Beneath the silver moon.

Distant silver moon

I woke with sun in the bright oak tree,

To see drifting clouds below,

I walked, I sang, I banged my stick,

And forgot to go home.

Happy on my own.

So I grew up in the kind oak tree,

Onwards still I climbed,

I grew long nails and an itchy beard,

Where insects came to hide.

And spiders came to hide.

On still nights in the dark oak tree,

Lions, bears, and wolves,

Curiously crept around me,

By tranquil mossy pools.

Deep and silent pools.

Seasons passed in the wise oak tree,

Until the moon was in reach,

I made my home in the highest heights,

Where strange sky creatures sleep.

Soft slow dreamers sleep.

There I joined those dreamers,

Dreaming with the old oak tree,

Beneath the bark, under tangled roots,

To a vast and quiet sea.

Shadowy memory sea.

I woke up in the strong oak tree,

My cat was licking my nose,

Her deep purr and warm soft fur,

Reminded me of home.

It was time to go home.

We left my camp in the old oak tree,

We made our slow way down,

I became eleven years old again,

As soon as I touched ground.

Back on solid ground.

As I walked from the old oak tree,

I heard Mum calling me,

To hurry up and wash my hands,

And get back inside for my tea.

We had fish and chips for tea.

Moon Sisters

The Moon has a lost sister
who lives at the bottom of the sea,
deep in a dark cavern
where no one has ever been.

She fell out with our moon
a million years ago,
She stormed off under the waves
and couldn't find her way home.

Now neither moon remembers
what they argued about,
There would be two moons in our sky
if it wasn't for that falling out.

Sometimes sailors hear
a sound from the sea floor,
a sad song that seems to say
I don't want to be alone anymore.

The Wizard's Fingers

When the wizard was asleep,
His fingers ran away,
To live in a rotten treestump,
And they still live there today.

They like to join in picnics,
Where their favourite kind of play,
Is hiding in your sandwiches,
Just to spoil your day.

Sparrow at the Picnic Table

picnic flitter
chipper
dip
diver darter
gone

back and bolder
swoop and squabble

ditta picka
crumb

from my fingers   ?
no

    but very close

picnic flitter
chipper
dip
diver darter
gone

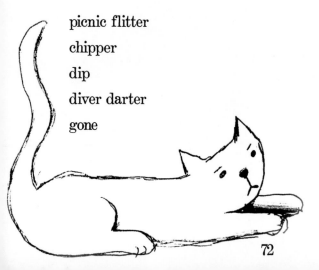

Tiny Nest

I took a dead old nest into school to show the class.

It was made of the old sheep wool you find on barbed wire fences
bits of grass, and some kind of stuffing from an old toy
the bird must have got from a bin

It looked like a dirty cloud of nothing.

But in the middle there were three tiny speckled eggs.
They looked impossible.

They looked like something an old fairy craftsman
made with tiny tools in the moonlight
as moths fluttered around his beard.

Harley said
Is that an actual nest?
Are they eggs? Will a bird hatch out?

He carefully picked one up
between his finger and thumb.

No one said anything.
We stared until he silently put it back.

Daisy and
The Wayward Wind

The End of Summer

The Wandering Wind

The Stone Buddha

Seasons Pass

Daisy

Daisy and The Wayward Wind

The End of Summer

When I was a child there was a big oak tree in our garden.

One evening, when I was about 8, I was lying under that tree. It was the last week of the Summer holidays and the branches above me were swaying in the wind. The hottest days of Summer were over and the coolness in the air felt good. My cat Daisy was wandering around nearby, sniffing, jumping and occasionally attacking my toes.

During that long Summer holiday Daisy and me had spent all our time together. Every night, she slept on my bed and every morning she woke me up by lying on my front and purring in my face. She jumped onto my lap at breakfast time and stared at my cereal. She followed me around every day. That Summer, I barely ever left the garden or spoke to other children. So Daisy and I spent the days looking for newts in the pond, digging up interesting bits of metal and bone and swaying on the rope swing that hung from the oak tree.

On this particular afternoon I lazily watched as she leapt onto the lowest branch of the oak tree. She walked along it, her tail swishing behind her. She jumped onto a higher branch, then an even higher one. She went higher and higher without looking back at all. Eventually all I could see was her tail moving through the leaves among the branches at the very top of the tree. And then I couldn't see her at all. I jumped up, suddenly panicking. Where had she gone?

She had disappeared like steam dissolving into the sky. I looked for her until it got dark but she was nowhere to be seen. That night I lay in bed for a long time worrying about her. But at last I fell asleep.

The Wandering Wind

That night I dreamt Daisy and Me

were climbing up the oak tree

chatting and singing and making plans

through the fading Summer leaves.

Among the swaying branches

we found Wind flying a kite.

Wind blew down to greet us.

Daisy meowed *Hi.*

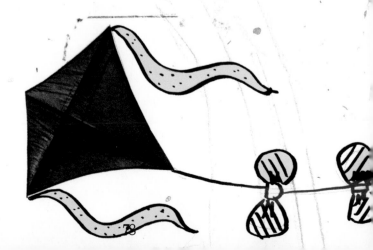

I asked Wind *Can you blow*

where in the world you like ?

Wind replied by lifting us

like feathers into the sky.

Wind swipped us up through swowling clouds

yippee high and wowly low

over humbly hills

and

mountain tops

smistral in the snow.

On a brellidy swell to Cragonook
where Raggle Naggle Soars

Far as any flewdays drift

Where no one has dreamed before

To the river of Lomorran

Past slopes of snoping snores

Through The Dark Forgottens

to a city of locked doors.

We found the sleeping giants of Orl

and slept in a giant's ear

We joined their symphostratal dreams

for a terramorgal year.

Until at last Wind

found Daisy and Me

And wearily blew us home

Daisy curled up on my bed.

But I woke up alone.

I looked everywhere for Daisy but she was still lost. The next day, we made 'lost cat' signs to put around the village but no one came forward.

On the last day of the holidays, I lay under the great tree staring up into the leaves. The swishing branches made a soothing sound like a lullaby. I fell asleep.

The Stone Buddha

I dreamed I was in the garden
sitting on the grass
the sun on my face
butterflies fluttering past,

But I missed my friend so much
I couldn't enjoy the day
so Wind came down blew in my ear
and took my sadness away,

I became so still and calm
I stayed there day after day
and became the wise stone buddha
and was happy to stay that way,

I learnt how birds need to fly
and insects need to crawl
and my friend needed her own adventures
in the big wide world,

But I could feel her all around
telling me it was time
to wake up, yawn and stretch
and get on with my life.

Daisy

Daisy is my family's cat,
But she is my best friend,
She's the only one allowed inside,
My box and blanket den.

I've filled it up with duvets,
And all our favourite foods,
I climb inside and very soon,
She follows me in for a snooze.

I always read her a book,
Before she goes to sleep,
She likes stories of koala bears,
They give her cosy dreams.

She curls up on my lap,
That's her favourite place,
She squeaks a quick meow,
When it's time to turn the page.

When we sleep the den is a ship,
And we are stowaways,
And the movement of her breathing,
Is the sighing of the waves.

Daisy is my family's cat,
But she is my best friend,
She's the only one allowed inside,
My box and blanket den.

The Spell Makers

My Cat, The Wind, and Me
search gardens yards and sheds
for bottle tops rusty rings
and springs from broken beds.

These are the kind of things we need
for our most basic recipes
like our spell for getting lost,
and for talking to hedgehogs.

My Cat, The Wind, and Me,
have stranger things we seek
we dig with spoons under bramble roots
searching for hen's tooth keys.

A hen's tooth key will unlock
a doorway made of London fog
at the top of a mile high pile of chairs,
in the empty high nowhere.

My Cat, The Wind, and Me
search by the moonlit sea
for Steven the ghost sailor
fishing on the beach.

If you kiss the salty lips
of a ghost sailor's fish
you will grow gills so you can breathe,
deep beneath the sea.

My Cat, The Wind, and Me
know the secret lanes
where scarecrows meet, drink wine and weep
at songs of the old days.

A single scarecrow tear
will rid you of all fear
if you mix it with moon tree ash
and a hummingbird's eyelash.

Yes, all you need to conquer fear
is a scarecrow tear,
moon tree ash,
and a hummingbird's eyelash.

A hummingbird's eyelash.

Fly with the Day Like a Runaway Kite
wake up moves to begin a wild day

Find a good spot that feels just right,
Stretch out your arms and close your eyes,

Take a deep breath and clear your mind,
And spin around some unsome times,

Now touch the ground and open your eyes,
And shake your arms to the top of the sky,

Now thank the ground and the air and light,
And fly with the day like a runaway kite,

Fly with the day like a runaway kite.

FURTHER TRAVELS IN THE
UNSOMEWHERE

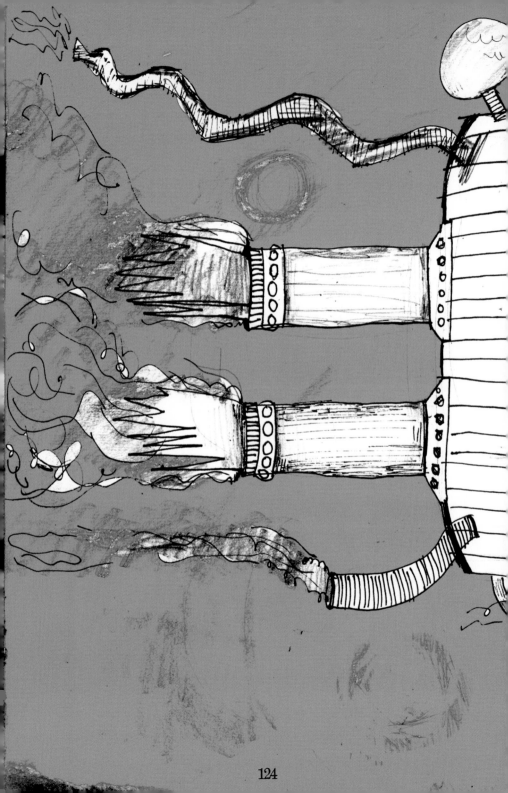

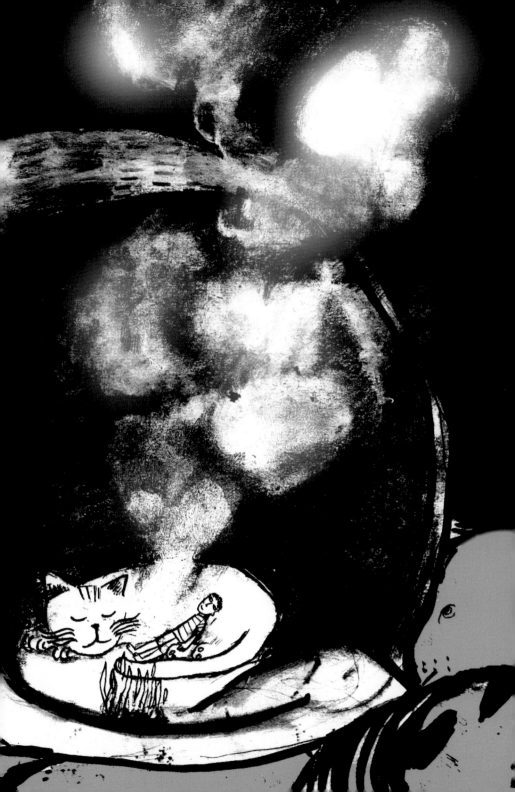

The Forest Out of Time

I woke with a head full of worries
so I went out to walk them away,
I found a good long stick
in the park where I used to play.

It fit just right in my hand.
It felt good by my side,
We walked together all day long
and lost all track of time.

We met Wendy Wildwood
with her hair down to her feet,
Her eyes grew wide when she saw
the stick I had with me.

She said *I can read these twists and knots*
and these ridges like winding streams
this stick will lead you to the place
you glimpsed once in a dream.

where the highest boughs sway in clouds,
summerfull and slow,
where the roots are old as loneliness,
dreaming as they grow.

You will find a place to plant your stick.
You will count to ninety nine.
It will become your own log cabin
with a bed and chair inside.

The trees will dream you a healing tale
for every lonely night
of seven years of solitude
in the forest out of time.

When you leave you'll forget those years
and just a moment will have passed,
but you'll carry those years of lonely healing
deep inside your heart.

And your highest boughs will sway in clouds
summerfull and slow,
your roots will be old as loneliness,
dreaming as you grow.